oops!...I did it again
britney spears

Exclusive distributors:
Music Sales Limited 8/9 Frith Street, London W1V 5TZ, England.
Music Sales Pty Limited 120 Rothschild Avenue, Rosebery, NSW 2018, Australia.

Order No.AM967120. ISBN 0-7119-8471-9. This book © Copyright 2000 by Wise Publications

The track "(I Can't Get No) Satisfaction" could not be included for copyright reasons.

Unauthorised reproduction of any part of this publication by any means including photocopying is an infringement of copyright.

Music arranged by Derek Jones. Music processed by Paul Ewers Music Design
Images courtesy of Jive Records
Printed in the United Kingdom by Caligraving Limited, Thetford, Norfolk.

Music Sales' complete catalogue describes thousands of titles and is available in full colour sections by subject, direct from Music Sales Limited.
Please state your areas of interest and send a cheque/postal order for £1.50 for postage to:
Music Sales Limited, Newmarket Road, Bury St. Edmunds, Suffolk IP33 3YB.

www.musicsales.com

£12·95

Oops!... I Did It Again

Words & Music by Max Martin & Rami Yacoub

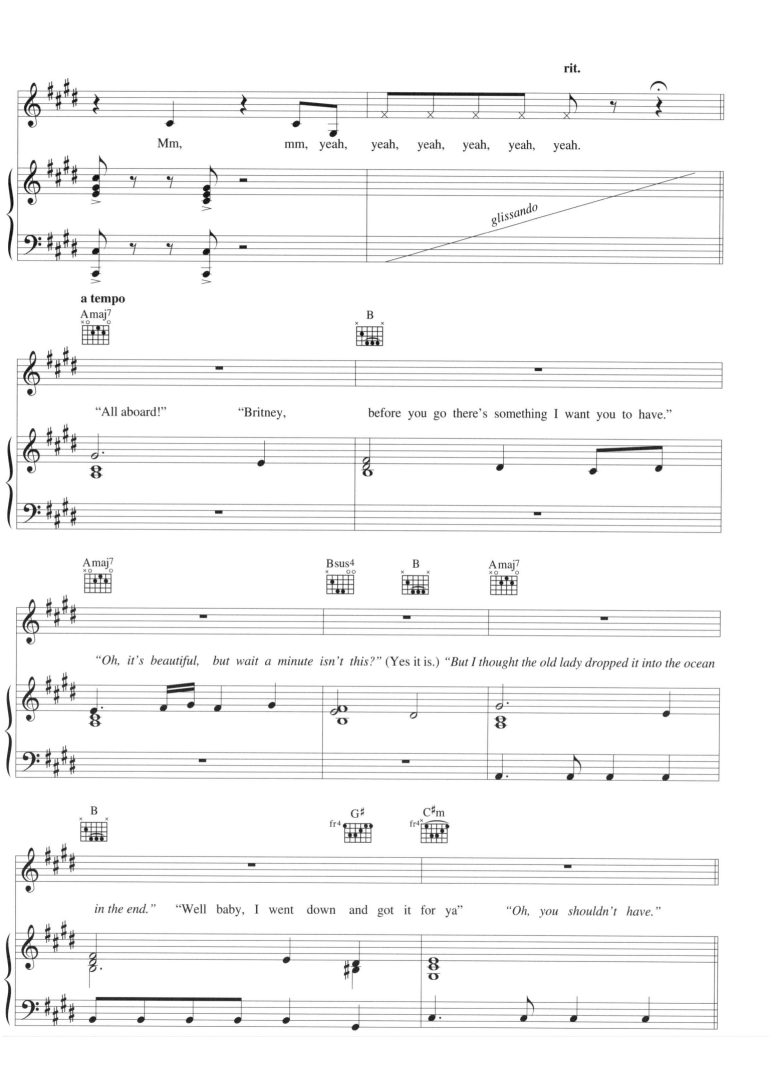

(Oops! I did it a-gain___ to your heart.___ Got-a lost

in this game, oh ba - by.___ Oops! You

think that I'm sent___ from a-bove.___ I'm not that in-no-cent.)

Oops! I did it a - gain.___ I've played with your heart,___

Verse 2:
You see my problem is this
I'm dreaming away
Wishing that heroes they truly exist
I cry watching the days
Can't you see I'm a fool in so many ways
But to lose all my senses
That is just so typically me.

Oops! I did it again *etc.*

Stronger

Words & Music by Max Martin & Rami Yacoub

Ooh — hey, — yeah. —

1. Hush, just stop, there's no-thing you can

do or say, ba - by. — I've had e - nough, —
(Verse 2 see block lyric)

Verse 2:
…than I ever thought that
I could be, baby
I used to go with the flow
Didn't really care 'bout me
You might think
That I can't take it
But you're wrong
Cos now I'm…

Stronger *etc.*

Don't Go Knockin' On My Door

Words & Music by Rami Yacoub, Jacob Schulze, Alexander Kronlund & Max Martin

Verse 2:
I can see it's no mystery
It's so clear to me what we had is all history
It's O.K. I can sleep at night
It will be alright
I can hear myself saying.

I am better off without you *etc.*

Don't Let Me Be The Last To Know

Words & Music by R.J. Lange, Shania Twain & Keith Scott

They say you say— we're so com-plete._____ But I need to hear— it

straight from— you if you want me to—— be-lieve

(Verse 2 see block lyric)

_____ it's— true._____ I've been wait-ing for—— so

long—— it hurts.—— I wan-na hear you say—— the—— words.— Please——

Verse 2:
Your body language says so much
Yeah, I feel it in the way you touch
But 'til you say the words it's not enough
C'mon and tell me you're in love, please.

Don't, don't let me be the last to know *etc.*

What U See (Is What U Get)

Words & Music by Per Magnusson, David Kreuger, Jörgen Elofsson & Rami Yacoub

Verse 2:
I know you watch me when I'm dancin'
When I party with my friends
I can feel your eyes on my back, baby
A-na-na
I can't have no chains around me
Baby can't you see
I could be anything you dream of
But I gotta feel free
You should never try to change me
I can be nobody else
And I like the way I am.

What you see *etc.*

Lucky

Words & Music by Max Martin, Rami Yacoub & Alexander Kronlund

I, I, ah, ah, ah.—— "Best actress, and the winner is…

Drums

Lucky!"

I, I, ah, ah, ah.——

Drums

"I'm Roger Johnson for Pop News standing outside the arena waiting for Lucky!"   "Is - n't—— she

"Oh my God, here she comes!"

Drums

love - ly,—— this Hol - ly - wood— girl?"——————

One Kiss From You

Words & Music by Steve Lunt

Verse 2:
I don't wanna hear my time will come
When it feels like it's already here
Oh, we should learn to walk before we run
But why go anywhere when you're so near
Cos when I reach out to you
So sad and confused
And feeling like I could cry
You dry my eyes.

Just one kiss from you *etc.*

Where Are You Now

Words & Music by Max Martin & Andreas Carlsson

now, what have you found? Where is your heart when I'm not a-

-round? Where are you now? You gotta let me know,

oh ba-by, so I can let you go.

1.

2.

N.C.

2. I can hear your voice

N.C.

Guitar

Verse 2:
I can hear your voice
The ring of yesterday
It seems so close to me
But yet so far away
I should let it out
To save what's left of me
And close the doors of doubt
Revive my dignity
But I can't go on
As long as I believe
Can't let go
When I keep wondering.

Where are you now *etc.*

Can't Make You Love Me

Words & Music by Kristian Lundin, Andreas Carlsson & Max Martin

Verse 2:
I have been through changes
But I'm still the girl you used to know
It's made me no different
So tell me why you had to go
Oh baby, I will trade the fancy cars
For a chance today
It's incomparable
I might be sitting with the movie stars
Everybody say that I just have it all.

But I can't make you love me *etc.*

When Your Eyes Say It

Words & Music by Diane Warren

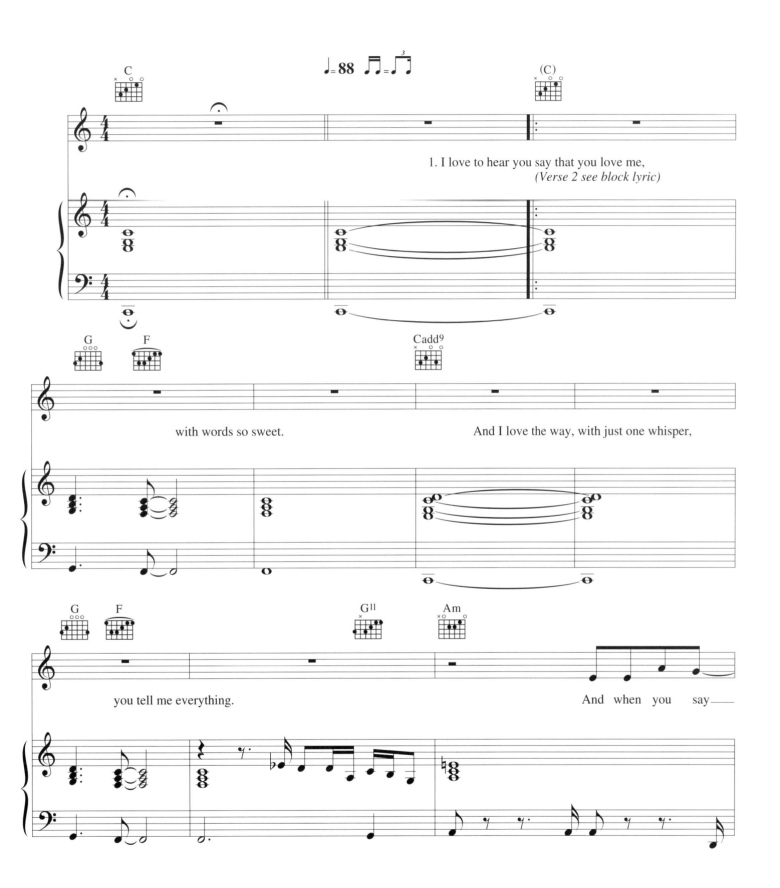

eyes tell me, (tell me) I know they're not___ tell - in' lies. They tell me___ (tell me)

all that you're feel - in' in - side.___ And it sounds so___ right___ when your

eyes say it,___ say___ it. And the words they say take my breath

a - way. no song___ ev - er sound - ed so sweet.___ I love ev -

Verse 2:
I love all the ways that you show me
You'll never leave
And the way your kisses
They always convince me
Your feelings run so deep
I love the things you say
And I love the love your touch conveys.

But when your eyes say it *etc.*

Dear Diary

Words & Music by Britney Spears, Jason Blume & Eugene Wilde

Verse 2:
Dear diary
Today I saw that boy
As he walked by I thought he smiled at me
And I wondered
Does he know what's in my heart?
I tried to smile, but I could hardly breathe
Should I tell him how I feel
Or would that scare him away?
Diary, tell me what to do
Please tell me what to say.

59

Girl In The Mirror

Words & Music by Jörgen Elofsson

1. There's a girl in my mir-ror, I
(Verse 2 see block lyric)
won-der who she is. Some-times I think I know her, some-times I real-ly wish I did. There's a sto-ry in her eyes,

Verse 2:

If I could, I would tell her
Not to be afraid
The pain that she's feeling
The sense of loneliness will fade
So dry your tears and rest assured
Love will find you like before
When she's looking back at me
I know nothing really works that easily.

Cos the girl in my mirror *etc.*

11/00 (38714)